MW00652803

THE
NORTH CAROLINA
QUIZ BOOK

Compiled from Our State *Quizzes*
by Alan Hodge

PUBLISHED BY MANN MEDIA INC., GREENSBORO, N.C.

The North Carolina Quiz Book
copyright © 2005 by Mann Media Inc.
All rights reserved.
Published by *Our State* magazine, Mann Media Inc.
P.O. Box 4552, Greensboro, N.C. 27404
(800)948-1409; www.ourstate.com
Printed in the United States by R.R. Donnelley & Sons

Publisher: Bernard Mann
Executive Vice President: Lynn Tutterow
Editor in Chief: Vicky Jarrett
Production Director: Cheryl Bissett
Marketing Director: Amy Jo Wood
Marketing Assistant: Debbie West

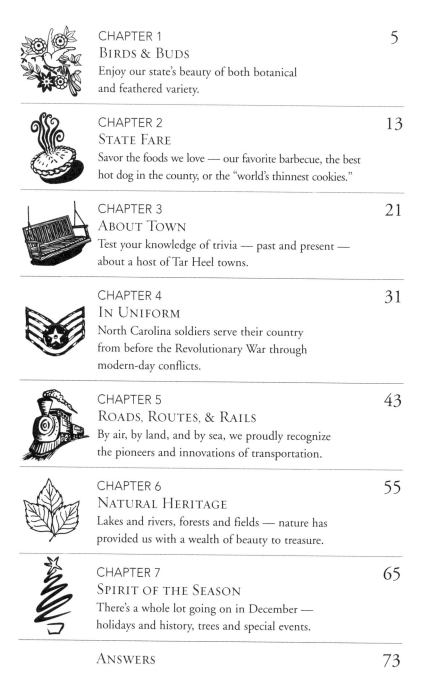

CHAPTER 1

BIRDS & BUDS

Enjoy our state's beauty of both botanical and feather variety as you test your knowledge of gardens, flowers, and plenty of birds.

Beautiful blooms

1. Sometimes growing to three feet in length, the arching stems of *Polygonatum biflorum* are festooned with small, bell-shaped white flowers. Found in North Carolina's deciduous forests, which plant is named after a wise biblical figure?
   A. Joshua's lily
   B. Solomon's seal
   C. David's flute

2. The leathery, evergreen leaves of the Spanish bayonet plant are accented during May and June in North Carolina with a cluster of creamy flowers reaching six feet in height. A native of our Coastal Plain, Spanish bayonet also goes by what name?
   A. Mesquite
   B. Guava
   C. Yucca

3. Frequently found in showy clumps along North Carolina roadsides, *Saponaria officinalis* goes by the common name of Bouncing Bet. Flowering from May until the first frost, it has what other name reflective of the texture of its crushed stems?
   A. Soapwort
   B. Toadflax
   C. Silkystem

4. Often used as a symbol of Dixie, the magnolia tree reaches the natural northern limit of its range in North Carolina. With fragrant flowers up to 12 inches across, the magnolia also goes by what other colloquial name?
   A. Plantation tree
   B. Redwood of the South
   C. Bull bay

5. Appearing in North Carolina bogs, wet pine barrens, and swamp margins as a shrub or tree, poison sumac shows small green flowers during May and June as well as colorful foliage in the fall. What other name is attributed to this plant, whose leaves can cause severe allergic reactions?
   A. Fireweed
   B. Thunderwood
   C. Lightningbush

6. Small, melon-shaped fruits about two inches long and lacy, pink blooms are prominent features of the passionflower. A native perennial to our state, *Passiflora incarnata* also goes by what name that comes from the sound its fruit makes when squeezed?
   A. Maypop
   B. Crackerball
   C. Snapdragon

7. With its large clusters of tiny, white flowers, Queen Anne's lace is a familiar sight in North Carolina fields and along roadsides. Blooming from May to September, this native Tar Heel wildflower also has what name reflective of its significant root structure?
   A. Beet flower
   B. Peanut plant
   C. Wild carrot

8. A glabrous annual standing as high as three feet, *Nicandra physalodes* is a North Carolina wildflower with pinkish blooms composed of a corolla of five fused petals. Found mainly in our mountain counties, this plant is originally from South America and goes by what name that includes a nation whose capital is Lima?
   A. Apple of Peru
   B. Cone of Colombia
   C. Fruit of the Falklands

9. The bright blue flowers of *Cichorium intybus* are a familiar sight along many North Carolina roadsides and fields. An introduced species, this weedy plant has roots that can be dried, then ground up and used as a substitute for coffee. Name this wildflower that blooms from June until October.
   A. Chicory
   B. Chick weed
   C. Chicarillum

10. Called coneflower by some, the wildflower *Rudbeckia hirta* has a dark brown center surrounded by two- to three-inch bright orange petals. Growing in nearly every Tar Heel county, this native species also goes by what feminine-sounding name?
    A. Bouncing Betty
    B. Jumping Jill
    C. Black-eyed Susan

11. Spatterdock is a native North Carolina wildflower whose yellow flowers are about two inches wide and characterized by a prominent stigma. Found at ponds, rivers, and swamps throughout the Piedmont and Coastal Plain, *Nuphar luteum* also has what bovine-sounding common name?
    A. Bull plant
    B. Cow lily
    C. Milkweed

Graceful gardens

12. The North Carolina Arboretum has more than 400 acres of plants, gardens, and trails, as well as a $2.5 million visitor center. Founded in 1986, the site was provided by the U.S. Forest Service and is located near what popular road?
    A. Blue Ridge Parkway
    B. Cherohala Skyway
    C. Foothills Parkway

13. The world-famous Biltmore Estate in Asheville has five formal gardens that include the Walled, Rose, Shrub, Spring, and Azalea gardens. The 40,000 azalea plants at Biltmore represent about how many species?
    A. 200 species
    B. 400 species
    C. 500 species

14. Founded in 1960 by the Asheville Garden Club, the Botanical Gardens at Asheville covers a 10-acre tract that's located at the University of North Carolina at Asheville campus. These gardens feature a fern and moss trail and what other special feature?
    A. Hayes Cabin
    B. Sculpture Garden
    C. Hydroponic Garden

15. Situated on the Duke University campus, the Sarah P. Duke Gardens comprise 55 acres of plants with a five-mile walking trail. Duke — who gave $20,000 to begin the gardens in the early '30s — is the wife of what member of the Duke family?
    A. James B. Duke
    B. Benjamin Duke
    C. Thaddeus Duke

16. The Elizabethan Gardens in Manteo date to 1951 and feature gardenias, roses, lilies, crape myrtles, and a statue of Virginia Dare sculpted in 1859. The Elizabethan Gardens are located at what fort?
    A. Fort Caswell
    B. Fort Anderson
    C. Fort Raleigh

17. More than 5,000 plant species and cultivars from 50 nations are on view at J.C. Raulston Arboretum's eight-acre site on the campus of North Carolina State University. J.C. Raulston Arboretum is part of what scholastic department at N.C. State?
    A. Department of Botany
    B. Department of Cultivation
    C. Department of Horticultural Science

18. Sandhills Community College in Moore County has a 27-acre public horticultural garden that features holly, conifers, camellias, and a wetlands trail. Sandhills Horticultural Gardens and the community college are located in what town?
    A. Pinehurst
    B. Cameron
    C. Pinebluff

19. Cape Fear Botanical Garden at Fayetteville has an 85-acre display of various plants as well as a large gazebo and natural amphitheater. This public garden is located at a fork between Cross Creek and what large river?
    A. Tar River
    B. Cape Fear River
    C. Neuse River

20. Spanish moss, live oaks, ponds, and acres of azaleas are features of Airlie Gardens near Wilmington. Airlie Gardens is part of the former estate of rice planter Pembroke Jones and is located near what sound?
    A. Wrightsville Sound
    B. Pamlico Sound
    C. Bogue Sound

21. Visitors to Daniel Boone Native Gardens in Boone can enjoy a variety of plants native to North America as well as a log cabin that once actually belonged to the Boone family. These gardens are situated near an outdoor theater that stages what drama each summer?
    A. *Strike at the Wind*
    B. *Horn in the West*
    C. *Unto These Hills*

Feathered friends

22. This bird of prey frequents areas of our state's coastal region and large inland bodies of water where it is often called "fish hawk." Name this cream-and-brown species with the scientific name *Pandion haliaetus* and a habit of returning to the same nest year after year.
    A. Osprey
    B. Heron
    C. Canada goose

23. One of the largest shorebirds found on the North Carolina coast, this black-and-white flyer with a bright red bill goes by the scientific name *Haematopus palliatus*. Identify this bird whose common name reflects its primary food of mollusks.
    A. Laughing gull
    B. Loon
    C. American oystercatcher

24. Found in nearly every part of the state, *Sturnus vulgaris* is a bird whose raucous and aggressive ways often displace other species. An Old World native, what bird type was released in New York's Central Park in March 1890 and by 1920 was already calling North Carolina home?
A. Sparrow
B. Starling
C. Pigeon

25. In addition to its common name and scientific moniker *Lanius ludovicianus*, this Tar Heel bird is also known as "butcherbird" for the habit of impaling prey on thorns and barbed wire. Which gray bird with a hooked bill also has a face mask?
A. Shrike
B. Barn owl
C. Red hawk

26. Benjamin Franklin wanted this crafty creature to be named our national bird instead of the bald eagle. Making a comeback in the Carolinas after nearly disappearing, *Meleagris gallopavo* loves to eat acorns and goes by what common name?
A. Grouse
B. Wild turkey
C. Pheasant

27. A colorful bird that makes its warm-weather home in North Carolina, *Passerina ciris* is generally seen along the coast and in certain inland locations. Name the sparrow-sized species with a purple head, green back, and red underparts.
A. Wood robin
B. Painted bunting
C. Red-crested woodpecker

28. The coloration of *Carduelis tristis* has earned this bird the nickname "wild canary." A year-round resident of North Carolina, which small flyer sometimes travels in large flocks?
A. Yellow warbler
B. Yellow-billed cuckoo
C. American goldfinch

29. Occasionally referred to as a "bullbat," this bird can be seen on summer evenings slicing through the Carolina sky on large, swept-back wings accented by a white patch. Scientifically known as *Chordeiles minor*, what jay-sized species loves to dine on insects and, when migrating, gathers in flocks numbering in the thousands?
A. Common nighthawk
B. Screech owl
C. Blackhawk

Azalea accolades

30. Although it is situated a few miles outside of Wilmington at Winnabow, which home with gardens, built in 1725 by "King" Roger Moore, is part of the public tour for the North Carolina Azalea Festival?
   A. Orton Plantation
   B. Live Oaks
   C. Somerset Plantation

31. The first North Carolina Azalea Festival was the idea of Dr. Houston Moore and was held in 1948. Which Wilmington businessman and early organizer of the festival is now known as the owner of Grandfather Mountain?
   A. Hugh Morton
   B. Hugh McColl
   C. Hugh Cummings

32. Many entertainers have performed at various venues during the North Carolina Azalea Festival's colorful history. In 2001, what singer — famous for his rendition of "I Left My Heart in San Francisco" — gave a performance at Trask Coliseum on the campus of the University of North Carolina at Wilmington?
   A. Frank Sinatra
   B. Tony Bennett
   C. Tony Curtis

33. The first Azalea Queen was Hollywood starlet Jacqueline White. During the crowning ceremony, which politician, governor from 1945 to 1949, placed the tiara upside down on White's head?
   A. R. Gregg Cherry
   B. J. Melville Broughton
   C. W. Kerr Scott

34. Featured on the 44th Annual Azalea Festival poster in 1991, which Wilmington landmark at the corner of Fifth and Market streets dates from 1859 and currently houses a history and design arts museum?
   A. Louise Cameron Wells House
   B. Bellamy Mansion
   C. Graystone Inn

35. What restored 1858 Wilmington building, located at 310 Chestnut Street, serves as a viewing stand for the Azalea Festival parade and also does double duty as a theater for the performing arts?
   A. Chandler's Wharf
   B. Burgwin-Wright House
   C. Thalian Hall

Answers on page 73.

CHAPTER 2
STATE FARE

The foods we love are near and dear to our hearts,
whether it's our favorite barbecue, the best hot dog in the county,
or a snack of the "world's thinnest cookies."

Tasty treats

1. Located beside U.S. Highway 64/70, this famous restaurant begun by Wayne Monk shares its name with the Davidson County seat.
   A. Lexington Barbecue
   B. Lexington Grille
   C. Lexington Diner

2. Morehead City is the home of this restaurant started in 1938 by "Capt." Tony Seamon and "Capt." Ted Garner with 12 stools in a rented building. It now seats 600 in a picturesque spot on the waterfront.
   A. El's Drive-In
   B. Spouter's Inn
   C. Sanitary Fish Market

3. Greensboro is the location of this popular eatery that traces its roots back to founder W.B. "Wisdom" Brown Aydelette. Today, the place is located near the campus of the University of North Carolina at Greensboro and offers a lunch of two hot dogs and a Coke for less than $3.
   A. Brown's Grille
   B. Yum Yum Better Ice Cream
   C. W.B.

4. This North Carolina treat started out as an idea in the basement of Salisbury grocer L.D. Peeler's store. Which product is still bottled in Salisbury and can be used in recipes ranging from barbecue sauce to punch to cake?
   A. Mint Cola
   B. Cheerwine
   C. Pepsi-Cola

5. In 1937, Vernon Rudolph and two partners started a company in Winston-Salem with $25 and a rented space across from Salem College. Name the "hot" commodity that is now sold in locations from New York to Los Angeles, California.
   A. Krispy Kreme
   B. Dunkin' Donuts
   C. Sara Lee

6. The egg industry is an important segment of the poultry business. North Carolina produces approximately what percentage of the nation's broiler hatching eggs?
   A. 20 percent
   B. 25 percent
   C. 30 percent

7. The largest independent pickle manufacturer in the United States, Mount Olive Pickle Company in Mount Olive dates back to 1926. Producing more than 70 million jars of pickles annually, this company is located at the corner of what two whimsically named streets?
   A. Cucumber and Vine
   B. Vinegar and Vine
   C. Pickle and Vine

8. T.W. Garner Food Company of Winston-Salem is known for its delicious jellies, jams, and preserves made from a variety of fruits. Name the company's other famous product, which puts pizzazz in many dishes.
   A. Boar and Castle Sauce
   B. Tabasco Sauce
   C. Texas Pete

9. Around the turn of the century, New Bern druggist Caleb Bradham invented a refreshment known as "Brad's Drink," which eventually was patented as Pepsi-Cola. Although he would receive scant credit and little money for his mark on history, Bradham received his patent for Pepsi in what year?
   A. 1895
   B. 1903
   C. 1910

10. Now a part of ConAgra Foods Snack Group, the second largest food company in the United States, GoodMark Foods Inc. of Garner orginally manufactured a popular spicy sausage snack that was born during the Depression and originally sold in Northeastern bars. What is the name of this convenience store staple?
    A. Slim Jim
    B. Beef Jerky
    C. Ham I Am

11. Dating back to 1930, Dewey's Bakery in Winston-Salem was founded by Dewey Wilkerson Sr. A division of Dewey's, Salem Baking Company is famous for baking "the world's thinnest cookie." Made of imported spices, flour, and molasses, this type of cookie originated in what Eastern European region?
    A. Transylvania
    B. Belgium
    C. Moravia

12. Several companies in North Carolina sell country ham, including Stadler's in Elon, Hancock's in Franklinville, and Johnston County Hams, which is located in what town that hosts an annual Ham and Yam Festival?
    A. Zebulon
    B. Smithfield
    C. Coats

13. In the 1920s, barbecuer Adam Scott first blended up a sauce recipe that's still one of the state's most popular brands. Patented in 1946 by Scott's son Martel Scott, Scott's Barbecue Sauce ships more than 750,000 bottles of product annually from its facility in what city on the Neuse River in Wayne County?
    A. Dobbersville
    B. Goldsboro
    C. Eureka

State specialties

14. Not only is the sweet potato our state's official vegetable, it's also an important cash crop with $64 million in receipts tallied in 2003. North Carolina ranks number one in the production of sweet potatoes and accounts for how much of the total grown nationally?
    A. 50 percent
    B. 40 percent
    C. 25 percent

15. The national champ in turkey production, North Carolina sent 45.5 million birds worth more than $420 million to consumers in 2002. What county ranks number one in turkey production, raising nearly one-fourth of the entire state output?
    A. Duplin County
    B. Robeson County
    C. Polk County

16. North Carolina's 11 million laying hens added more than $220 million to the state's economy in 2002 with an output of 2.5 billion eggs. What is the approximate average number of eggs each hen lays in a year's time?
    A. 125 eggs
    B. 225 eggs
    C. 300 eggs

17. Aquaculture is on the rise in North Carolina. In a recent year, our state's aquaculturists raised 4.4 million pounds of trout that sold for $5.7 million. Nationally ranked second in production behind Idaho, there are about how many Tar Heel trout-raising farms in operation?
    A. 46
    B. 79
    C. 82

18. Call them goobers or penders, peanuts are an important cash crop in North Carolina with 100,000 acres harvested in 2003, for a yield of 320 million pounds. How does North Carolina rank nationally in peanut output?
    A. 3rd place
    B. 4th place
    C. 5th place

19. Grapes are an ever-increasing crop in North Carolina with 2,300 tons produced in 2002 on 850 bearing acres. What type of grape is not only grown commercially but is also our official North Carolina state fruit?
    A. Concord
    B. Muscadine
    C. Scuppernong

20. Not only is milk our official state drink, but also products from North Carolina's 61,000 dairy cows added $228 million to the Tar Heel economy in 2004. How much milk does a North Carolina cow produce, on average, in one year?
    A. 17,000 pounds
    B. 9,000 pounds
    C. 5,000 pounds

Diners' delights

21. Known for generous family-style portions, the restaurant at historic Jarrett House dates back to 1884 when its original structure was built by William Dills. Once a stop on the Western North Carolina Railroad, Jarrett House is part of what Jackson County town?
    A. Dillsboro
    B. Dilltown
    C. Dillburg

22. Shatley Springs Inn and Restaurant near Crumpler was once a spa where visitors came to partake of waters said to have healing effects. Fried chicken, country ham, biscuits, and vegetables are drawing cards at this historic restaurant located in what county?
A. Buncombe
B. Jefferson
C. Ashe

23. A Tar Heel favorite, the Nu-Wray Inn in Burnsville dates back to 1833 when it was built of constructed logs. Dishes at the Nu-Wray's restaurant include cream gravy, tipsy cake, and smothered lettuce salad. Built on the town square in Burnsville, the inn is included on what prestigious list?
A. National Register of Historic Places
B. National Trust Registry
C. North Carolina Historic Sites Roster

24. Listed on the National Register of Historic Places since 1995, Josephine's Restaurant at Lone Beech in Marion served lunch and dinner in a refined atmosphere for years before it closed. The 7,000-square-foot house in which Josephine's was located was built in 1902 as a cottage ordered from what catalog?
A. Sears
B. Montgomery Ward
C. J.C. Penney

25. Featuring a fine restaurant, pub, and art gallery, the Harvey Mansion in New Bern is a 200-year-old structure that was once a home, office, and warehouse for planter and businessman John Harvey. Located at 221 Front Street, the Harvey Mansion sits by what river?
A. Tar River
B. Cape Fear River
C. Trent River

26. Located on 28 acres of rolling Henderson County landscape, the Woodfield Inn dates back to 1852 when it served as a stagecoach station. Featuring three dining rooms seating 200 guests, the restaurant at the Woodfield Inn stands near what famous author's residence?
A. Thomas Wolfe
B. Carl Sandburg
C. Fred Chappell

27. On the National Register of Historic Places since 1972, Mast Farm dates back to the late 1700s. Now a gracious lodging and dining establishment, the Mast Farm Inn is located in what Watauga County town whose name means "valley of the cross?"
A. Crusi Valle
B. Val Crucifix
C. Valle Crucis

28. An architectural gem of the Victorian age, Richmond Hill Inn in Asheville features elegant lodging in each of its 36 rooms as well as fine dining in the mansion's Gabrielle's restaurant, which has won what prestigious AAA award for its cuisine?
A. Four Diamond Award
B. Silver Spoon Award
C. Traveler's Best Award

29. Charles and Mary Clawson, immigrants to North Carolina from Sweden and Ireland, originally owned Clawson's 1905 Restaurant and Pub in Beaufort. On Front Street, Clawson's building has been used for many purposes, including a bakery and what other type of store operated by the Clawsons?

A. Harness shop
B. Grocery
C. Fish house

30. In the early 20th century, Captain Amos Frye built the rustic Fryemont Inn and its restaurant, which are listed on the National Register of Historic Places. Featuring native trout prepared at least four ways, the Fryemont Inn and its dining room are located in what Swain County town once known as Charleston?
A. Cherokee
B. Cullowhee
C. Bryson City

31. Opened in 1882, the Green Park Inn features a championship-quality golf course in addition to elegant accommodations and gourmet meals. The Green Park's Laurel Room Restaurant is located in Caldwell County on U.S. Highway 321 in what town?
A. Boone
B. Blowing Rock
C. Candler

Answers on page 74.

CHAPTER 3

About Town

Test your knowledge of trivia — past and present —
about a host of Tar Heel towns.

Port cities

1. An important part of the transportation scene for more than two centuries, Wilmington's position on the Cape Fear River made it an ideal seaport. Part of a trade zone originally called the Port of Brunswick, Wilmington was incorporated in what year?
   A. 1710
   B. 1739
   C. 1779

2. Port development in Morehead City began in the 1850s. Originally called Shepherd's Point, the port city named for North Carolina governor John Motley Morehead (1796-1866) is located along what river?
   A. Tar River
   B. Neuse River
   C. Newport River

3. In 1949, the General Assembly approved $7.5 million in bonds for construction and improvement of North Carolina ports. What year during the Korean War era were terminals completed in Wilmington and Morehead City that were equipped to handle oceangoing ships?
   A. 1952
   B. 1956
   C. 1957

4. In 1945, the state legislature created the N.C. State Ports Authority. In addition to the ports of Wilmington and Morehead City, the N.C. Ports Authority operates a small boat harbor near the entrance to the Cape Fear River downstream from Wilmington at what town?
   A. Town Creek
   B. Winnabow
   C. Southport

5. Excellent highway access to the ports at Wilmington and Morehead City has done much to expedite the exchange of both imports and exports from those facilities. In Wilmington, the State Port is just off U.S. Highway 421. What major road leads to the docks at Morehead City?
   A. U.S. Highway 17
   B. U.S. Highway 70
   C. N.C. Highway 49

6. The Port of Morehead City recently saw completion of a new $8 million railroad trestle to a nearby island where the port plans expansion. The new trestle replaces a wooden structure originally built in 1907. To what island, the site of a large aviation fuel depot, does the trestle go?
   A. Radio Island
   B. Roanoke Island
   C. Bald Head Island

Namesakes

7. A college town, Transylvania County's seat also is the home of a popular summer music festival and the Cradle of Forestry in America historic site. Name this community incorporated in 1889 and titled for a Revolutionary War surgeon.
   A. Brendletown
   B. Brevard
   C. Boone

8. The little community of Jackson Hill in Davidson County dates back to 1828. Located on N.C. Highway 8 just a few miles from the Yadkin River, Jackson Hill was named for what Southern military man?
   A. Andrew Jackson
   B. Stonewall Jackson
   C. Jackson Browne

9. Perched in Perquimans County between the Little and Perquimans rivers, Durants Neck takes its name from George Durant who settled nearby during the mid-1600s. Name the large body of fresh water near Durants Neck that was originally known as the Sea of Rawnocke.
   A. Lake Norman
   B. Rattan Bay
   C. Albemarle Sound

10. A textile town in Gaston County, Bessemer City dates back to the Victorian era. Bessemer City was named after Sir Henry Bessemer (1813-1898), who discovered the process of making what important modern metal?
    A. Steel
    B. Aluminum
    C. Titanium

11. Located on a site that was originally a militia muster grounds before campaigns against the Indians and the Battle of Kings Mountain, Newland was incorporated in 1913. Flanked by the Linville and Toe rivers, Newland is in what county?
A. McDowell County
B. Avery County
C. Ashe County

12. Once called Lonesome Valley by an early settler homesick for his native Virginia, Henderson in Vance County takes its name from 19th-century jurist Leonard Henderson. That Virginian would probably be surprised to see what teeming highway skimming the outskirts of Henderson these days?
A. I-26
B. I-95
C. I-85

13. Incorporated in 1852, the seat of Montgomery County was laid out as early as 1843. Bisected by N.C. Highway 24/27, this Tar Heel town's name is said to have come from either a 19th-century UNC trustee, a former member of the General Assembly, or what ancient Mediterranean city?
A. Athens
B. Troy
C. Memphis

14. Formed at the junction of N.C. Highway 16 and the Alexander Railroad, this Tar Heel town dates back to 1847 and takes its name from the 12th President of the United States. Name this town called after the man known as "Old Rough and Ready."
A. Taylorsville
B. Jacksonville
C. Lincolnton

15. Not as populous as the city of the same name in Ohio, North Carolina's town of Cleveland is located about 10 or so miles northwest of Salisbury in Rowan County. Originally known as Third Creek, Cleveland takes its name after what former United States commander-in-chief?
A. Theodore Cleveland
B. Benjamin Cleveland
C. Grover Cleveland

16. Our state's only deepwater port north of Wilmington, Morehead City is situated on Bogue Sound and the

Newport River and is located in what county?

A. New Hanover County
B. Onslow County
C. Carteret County

17. The seat of Stanly County, Albemarle is a thriving North Carolina city that also offers wilderness recreation in nearby Uwharrie National Forest. Albemarle takes its name from George Monck (1608-1670), who also went by what title?

A. Lords Proprietor of Carolina
B. Carolina's Royal Gubernator
C. Royal Carolina Highness

Queen City

18. When British troops under the command of Lord Cornwallis entered the Charlotte area in September 1780, patriots met them with sharp resistance. After a brisk fight along East Trade and Tryon streets, the redcoats referred to the town as what type of nest of rebellion?

A. Hornet's nest
B. Squirrel's nest
C. Crow's nest

19. Charlotte's first professional baseball team was formed in 1902 as a member of the Carolina League but folded before the end of the season. In 1908, baseball returned to Charlotte, and the team won the Carolina Association pennant. What nickname, recurring later in Charlotte sports life, did this team have?

A. Charlotte Stings
B. Charlotte Hornets
C. Charlotte Mudcats

20. Rail transport has been an important factor in the growth of Charlotte since the mid-19th century. On October 21, 1852, the first passenger train of the Charlotte and South Carolina Railroad pulled into town and was greeted by brass bands and 20,000 revelers. From what central South Carolina city had the train come?

A. Aiken
B. Georgetown
C. Columbia

21. During the Civil War, many Charlotte men marched to battle in companies such as the Hornets' Nest Rifles and the Charlotte Grays. Some of them had attended the North Carolina Military Academy in Charlotte founded by which future Confederate general, who is buried near Davidson College?
   A. Garibaldi Stewart
   B. D.H. Hill
   C. R.L. "Pineknot" Helton

22. One of the current largest manufacturers of snack foods in the country can trace its roots back to 1913. What company, named for its founder, still turns out millions of packs of peanut butter sandwich crackers every year from its Charlotte plant?
   A. Lance Inc.
   B. Calvin's Crackers
   C. Famous Amos

23. The first passenger airline landing in Charlotte took place on December 10, 1938, when a Curtis Condor plane touched down. To help pilots find their way, the Charlotte Airport, now the site of Charlotte/Douglas International, was laid out near the junction of railroad tracks and what river?
   A. Broad River
   B. Rocky River
   C. Catawba River

24. On May 20, 1775, when delegates called by Colonel Thomas Polk gathered at the courthouse in Mecklenburg County, they drafted what document said to be the first official act of defiance to King George III in the American colonies?
   A. Charlottetown Resolves
   B. Mecklenburg Articles
   C. Mecklenburg Declaration of Independence

25. Charlotte's first radio station began in the basement of Fred Laxton's home in 1920 with a set of tubes he had received from General Electric Company. On April 10, 1922, the station, previously known as 4XD, was licensed commercially under what call letters?
   A. WGIV
   B. WSOC
   C. WBT

26. In July 1917, Charlotte was selected as the site for a new camp designed to train soldiers

for service in World War I. When it became fully operational, it was the only Army camp in the South to hold three divisions and, at times, up to 60,000 men. Name this facility, which took its moniker from a Revolutionary War general.

A. Camp Greene
B. Camp Ellis
C. Camp Hudson

How's that?

27. Situated in Mitchell County along the Toe River, this community on N.C. Highway 226A south of Bakersville takes its name from a type of cloth.

A. Washrag
B. Bandana
C. Dishrag

28. This community shares its name with several creeks, gaps, and peaks in our mountains. Located in northeast Henderson County, what area is called by the type of animal seen around there?

A. Bearwallow
B. Hogwallow
C. Deerbog

29. Apiarists will like the name of the community located in north Yancey County near Bald Mountain Creek. Identify this area where a sweet discovery led to its name.

A. Sugarhill
B. Sorghum Ridge
C. Bee Log

30. Eastern Swain County contains this community, one of five in the Qualla Boundary. A Cherokee word that references its name helps identify what spot on the Oconaluftee River?

A. Wolf Laurel
B. Bear Path
C. Birdtown

31. Good luck must be a common denominator for those who live in this Henderson County community. Situated in a bend of the French Broad River, what area is about three miles northeast of Etowah?

A. Horse Shoe
B. Rabbit's Foot
C. Seven Devils

32. Folks who lived in this central Mitchell County community were known for their laid-back ways that gave the spot its name. Located on Cane Creek, what area was christened with its current name back in 1890?
    A. Lazy Lick
    B. Loafers Glory
    C. Resting Ridge

33. The discovery by hunters that their cooking utensils had provided animals a snack was the genesis for this Macon County community. Name the area that's situated between the beginning of Tessentee Creek and Piney Knob Fork.
    A. Clean Plate
    B. Pot Scrubber
    C. Lickskillet

34. First known as Lakewood, this Henderson County community is near the South Carolina state line. Also close to Lake Summit, what area takes its name from a type of clothing?
    A. Overcoat
    B. Tuxedo
    C. Top Hat

35. This Mitchell County community has the distinction of being the site of the first free public library (1887) in North Carolina, as well as the third county library in the nation. Identify this landmark spot that's named after the man who started the institution with 15,000 volumes.
    A. Turnersburg
    B. Wing
    C. Youngsville

36. Located near Cherry Mountain and on Roberson Creek in Rutherford County, this community was named in the late 1800s by storekeeper J.W. Biggerstaff. A celestial display above the mountain gives this area what name?
    A. Moonshine
    B. Rainbow
    C. Sunshine

On the home front

37. On December 7, 1941, the Japanese attacked Pearl Harbor. In protest, the Durham County town of Oyama — named after a city in Japan — changed its name to Few after Dr. William Few, the first president of what university?
    A. Appalachian State University
    B. Campbell University
    C. Duke University

38. March 8, 1865, witnessed the arrival of both wings of General William T. Sherman's army in North Carolina. On that date, men of the Fifteenth Corps camped five miles west of Laurinburg at what town, now on U.S. Highway 74 just southeast of Old Hundred?
A. Red Springs
B. Laurel Hill
C. Masons Cross

39. On March 11, 1865, elements of Sherman's army reached Fayetteville. A major objective was the former Federal arsenal that had provided thousands of rifles and other ordnance for the Confederacy. By the time Federal troops had arrived, much of the arsenal's machinery had been moved to what coal-mining town?
A. Bombay
B. Egypt
C. Shanghai

40. Although Union soldiers occupied Raleigh, some shots still were fired in the area. Two miles west of Raleigh on Hillsboro Road, Sherman's cavalry under General Judson Kilpatrick had a sharp fight with horsemen in gray. This skirmish was followed by another shootout 10 miles farther west near what town north of Cary?
A. Rolesville
B. Morrisville
C. Eagle Rock

41. One of North Carolina's signers of the Declaration of Independence, William Hooper currently lies buried at Guilford Courthouse National Military Park. Hooper was first interred in what Orange County town that was not only his home, but also was the site for the Third Provincial Congress in 1775?
A. Hillsborough
B. Caldwell
C. Carr

42. Fought on February 27, 1776, the Battle of Moores Creek Bridge was a Patriot victory and is said to have prevented an impending British invasion of the South. The site of the battle, now Moores Creek National Military Park, is located 25 miles northwest of Wilmington near what town?
A. Currie
B. Delco
C. Bolivia

Answers on page 75.

CHAPTER 4

IN UNIFORM

Since before the Revolutionary War launched North Carolinians
into battle for their country through modern-day conflicts,
patriotic men and women have been rallying for the cause of freedom.

Tar Heel troops

1. A native of Greensboro, U.S. Army Air Corps Major George Preddy had scored 26.83 aerial victories over Europe before his death on Christmas Day, 1944. What type of plane was Preddy flying when he scored all but three of these victories?
   A. P-40 Tomahawk
   B. P-47 Thunderbolt
   C. P-51 Mustang

2. Major William Chronicle was born in Gaston (formerly Lincoln) County. During the American Revolution, Chronicle lost his life on October 7, 1780, leading his South Fork Boys against Loyalists in what battle described as a "turning point of the Revolution in the South?"
   A. Cowpens
   B. Guilford Courthouse
   C. Kings Mountain

3. A native of Lincolnton born on May 31, 1837, Stephen Dodson Ramseur became at age 27 the youngest West Point-educated major general in the Confederate Army. Ramseur was mortally wounded leading his troops during what battle in Virginia on October 19, 1864?
   A. Cedar Creek
   B. Antietam
   C. Chancellorsville

4. One of the most successful officers in the United States Army during the War of 1812 was Benjamin Forsyth, who rose to the rank of lieutenant colonel before his death in 1814. Present-day Forsyth County is named for him and was formed in 1849 from what county?
   A. Randolph County
   B. Stokes County
   C. Rowan County

5. A native of Buncombe County, Zebulon Vance was not only a two-time governor of our state but also a U.S. senator. Before his first election as governor in 1862, Vance had seen action as a Confederate officer in places such as the Battle of New Bern. What rank did Vance hold in his regiment, the 26th North Carolina?
   A. Captain
   B. Major
   C. Colonel

6. North Carolina contributed 86,000 troops in World War I, including one major general, three brigadier generals, and

three rear admirals. Brigadier General Samson Faison from Duplin County had as one of his assignments command of the famed 30th Infantry Division that broke what German line?

A. Hindenburg Line
B. Maginot Line
C. Kaiser Wilhelm Line

7. U.S. Navy Lieutenant Rufus Herring from Roseboro received the Congressional Medal of Honor for continuing to operate his LCI ship during intense fighting on February 17, 1945. What volcanic island, topped by Mount Suribachi, was the location of this battle?

A. Okinawa
B. Iwo Jima
C. Guadalcanal

8. Steve Ritchie from Reidsville became the only U.S. Air Force ace during the Vietnam War. Flying his F-4 Phantom fighter jet, Ritchie shot down how many North Vietnamese Mig-21 planes to earn the title "ace?"

A. 5
B. 10
C. 12

9. The Spanish-American War in 1898 saw troops from North Carolina take part in the action. The only African American in the U.S. Army to rise from the rank of captain to lieutenant colonel in command of a regiment of other African-American volunteers was C.S.L.A. Taylor from what "Hornet's Nest" county?

A. Cabarrus
B. Mecklenburg
C. Iredell

10. During Operation Desert Shield and Desert Storm in Kuwait and Iraq, General Walter Boomer was in command of U.S. Marine Corps troops there. General Boomer retired from the Marines as assistant commandant in 1994. His hometown is what community on U.S. Highway 258 in Northampton County?

A. Galatia
B. Potecasi
C. Rich Square

Civil War

11. After leaving South Carolina in February 1865, General William T. Sherman's troops began marching to the Tar Heel state with the eventual goal of linking up with Union forces in Virginia. One wing of Sherman's army crossed what river between Hamlet and Wadesboro to enter North Carolina?
A. Pee Dee River
B. Tyger River
C. Catawba River

12. By the time Sherman's troops entered North Carolina, they had been cut off from their supply bases in Savannah, Georgia, for weeks. What North Carolina seaport city, known as the "lifeline of the Confederacy," did Sherman hope to use as a depot for provisioning his soldiers?
A. New Bern
B. Washington
C. Wilmington

13. By March 15, 1865, Sherman had his entire army across the Cape Fear River in North Carolina and was aiming for Goldsboro. On the Confederate side was what general whose earlier injuries at the battle of Seven Pines, Virginia, in May 1861, had moved Robert E. Lee into command of the South's forces in the Old Dominion?
A. Joseph Johnston
B. Stonewall Jackson
C. Richard "Baldy" Ewell

14. The largest battle ever fought on Tar Heel soil took place during March 19-21, 1865, between 25,000 Confederates and 60,000 of Sherman's Union soldiers. The 6,000-acre Bentonville Battlefield is now a North Carolina Historic Site located off U.S. Highway 701 in what county seated by Smithfield?
A. Richmond County
B. Johnston County
C. Sampson County

15. In a humorous incident during Sherman's march through North Carolina, Union cavalry leader General Judson Kilpatrick and a lady companion were surprised in bed near the Solemn Grove community by attacking Confederate horsemen. This dawn skirmish, in which Kilpatrick barely escaped capture, has come to be known as the battle of what?
A. Kilpatrick's Pants
B. The Rude Awakening
C. Surprise on the Wabash

16. Four years to the day after Charleston's Fort Sumter surrendered to the Confederacy, Sherman's troops, near Smithfield, received the electrifying news that Robert E. Lee had capitulated to General Ulysses S. Grant several days before. On what date in April 1865 did Sherman's men hear that report?
    A. April 1, 1865
    B. April 12, 1865
    C. April 15, 1865

17. With Federal infantry approaching Raleigh, Governor Zebulon Vance wrote a letter to Sherman requesting an interview to determine how a suspension of hostilities might be arranged. A former soldier himself, Vance had earlier in the war been colonel of what regiment?
    A. 26th North Carolina
    B. 28th North Carolina
    C. 49th North Carolina

Sites and sounds

18. The oldest house still standing in Mecklenburg County was built in 1774 and is now on the grounds of the Charlotte Museum of History. This stone dwelling was the scene of serious debate in 1775 when what patriot/owner discussed with his peers the upcoming Mecklenburg Declaration of Independence?
    A. Leonidas Kasmer
    B. Hezekiah Alexander
    C. Marcus Francis Brendle

19. Constructed in 1773, the Alston House near Sanford is a State Historic Site. The spot where Whigs and Tories clashed in 1780-81, this dwelling was also the home of North Carolina Governor Benjamin Williams (1799-1802, 1807-1808). What other popular name is the Alston House called?
    A. White House
    B. Rock House
    C. House in the Horseshoe

20. The final resting place of several veterans of the Battle of Kings Mountain, Goshen Cemetery near Belmont in Gaston County is said to have been the first cemetery west of the Catawba River. In addition to the Kings Mountain Boys, several other Revolutionary-period graves can be found in this plot just a half mile from what college?
    A. Belmont Abbey College
    B. Gaston College
    C. Kings College

21. From 1781-1785, Gilbert Town near Rutherfordton was the seat of Rutherford County. During the American Revolution, an impetuous British officer camped near Gilbert Town issued a rude ultimatum to the local patriots demanding they cease resisting the crown. Name this brash British leader who was killed just a short time later at Kings Mountain.
A. Nathaniel Greene
B. David Caldwell
C. Patrick Ferguson

22. A marker on U.S. Highway 421 in Chatham County pinpoints the site where an important source of munitions for North Carolina patriots was once located. The furnace for Wilcox Iron Works stood about 100 yards southeast of the road near what Chatham community that was named for a United States president's home?
A. Arlington
B. Ingleside
C. Mount Vernon Springs

23. During the revolution, many Scots Highlanders who were crown sympathizers met at a Presbyterian church near Lillington in Harnett County. Although the present church on N.C. Highway 27 was erected in 1895, the first went up in 1757 and was given what delicious name?
A. Catfish Church
B. Barbecue Church
C. Angel Cake Church

24. The Edenton Tea Party, a gathering of more than 50 ladies of the town on October 25, 1774, in support of American independence, has been called the "earliest known instance of political activity on the part of women in the American colonies." In Edenton today, the site is marked by a large, bronze teapot mounted on what item?
A. Ship anchor
B. Revolutionary War cannon
C. Cast iron oven

25. The site where several of Lord Cornwallis' troops were buried during the revolution, Old English Cemetery in Rowan County, was granted to the city in 1770 by the British government. In what Rowan town, also the site of a national cemetery, is this graveyard located?
A. China Grove
B. Badin
C. Salisbury

Company calls

26. Organized at Troy in Montgomery County in March 1862, Company F of the 44th Regiment saw action in eastern North Carolina as well as Virginia. Never a group to hide in a wooden horse, Company F went by what name?
    A. Hellenistic Heathens
    B. Trojan Regulators
    C. Grecian Grapplers

27. Company K of the 26th Regiment N.C. Troops signed up in Wadesboro on July 1861 and was trained at Camp Carolina in Wake County. What confederate crowd named itself after a river that flowed through its native Anson County?
    A. Pee Dee Wildcats
    B. Lumber River Yankee Lashers
    C. Rocky River Ruffians

28. Another 26th N.C. Troops outfit was Company B from Union County. This group was in the thick of the fighting at Gettysburg and lost several men. Company B used the surname of a former United States president known as "Old Hickory" to form what title of their own?
    A. Monroe Marauders
    B. Waxhaw Washington Warriors
    C. Waxhaw Jackson Guards

29. Company E of the 28th North Carolina saw fighting at Chickamauga and other areas in the Civil War's western theater. Mountain men from the hills and dales beyond Asheville formed Company E, which took what name after a county whose seat is Waynesville?
    A. Haywood Fire Shooters
    B. Henderson Heroes
    C. Polk County Patriots

30. Raised in Burke and Catawba counties in October 1861, Company K of the 35th Regiment took part in the Seven Days' battle in 1862. Not men who depended on their hairstyles to gain strength, Company K nonetheless chose what name?
    A. Burke and Catawba Beehives
    B. Burke and Catawba Crewcuts
    C. Burke and Catawba Samsons

31. Company D of the 27th North Carolina was Lenoir County's first Confederate volunteer unit and consisted of 59 men. Company D was known by what nickname that reflected both an area near Lenoir County and a championship Georgia baseball team of the 20th century?
A. Tuckahoe Braves
B. Sand Hill Crackers
C. Woodington Peaches

32. Heroes at the Battle of Sharpsburg in September 1862, Company E, 30th Regiment N.C. Troops had originally formed up in the Duplin County town of Teachy. Company E named itself after its home county and what important Tar Heel pine product?
A. Duplin Pineknots
B. Duplin Resin Raisers
C. Duplin Turpentine Boys

33. The skilled horsemen of Company K, 1st Regiment, trained at Camp Woodfin near Asheville in July 1861 before going into action. Eventually fighting in 94 battles, Company K chose what name after the North Carolina mountain area that is today a national forest?
A. Blue Ridge Bandits
B. Nantahala Rangers
C. Fontana Furies

34. When mustered in at Smithfield in May 1861, Company E, 14th Regiment N.C. Volunteers, was 83 men strong. Although Tar Heels rather than Texans did the fighting, Company E nonetheless adopted what nickname that might be associated with the Confederacy's westernmost state?
A. Longhorn Legion
B. Lone Star Boys
C. Carolina Cowboys

35. Tyrrell County men strode forth in May 1861 to sign up for Confederate service in what would become the 32nd Regiment North Carolina Troops. Commanded by Edmund Brabble of Currituck County, the Tyrrell contingent of the 32nd went by what nickname that was inspired by native Tar Heel grapes and a North Carolina river of the same name?
A. Scuppernong Grays
B. Concord Cadets
C. Chablis Chargers

36. One of five Confederate companies raised in Rutherford County in 1861, Company B of the 34th Regiment North Carolina Troops took part in the 1863 Battle of Chancellorsville. No doubt delivering many a sting to the Federals, Company B went by what nickname?
    A. Rutherford Rascals
    B. Forest City Foragers
    C. Sandy Run Yellow Jackets

37. Cited for bravery at the Battle of Malvern Hill in July 1861, this company took its name from what Tar Heel waterway that flows through the heart of Chatham County?
    A. Haw River Boys
    B. Meherrin River Musketeers
    C. Waccamaw River Warriors

38. Company A of the 22nd Regiment North Carolina Troops was unique in that four brothers from a family named Deal all served in that unit. Seeing action at battles such as Cold Harbor, the Deals and their comrades in Company A went by what nickname that reflected their home county seated by Lenoir?
    A. Catawba Cavaliers

    B. Caldwell Rough and Ready Boys
    C. Wilkes Wild Bunch

Generally speaking

39. A native of Tyrrell County, Brigadier General James Johnston Pettigrew was a graduate of the University of North Carolina at age 15 and served before the Civil War as a professor at the U.S. Naval Observatory. Pettigrew was mortally wounded after the Battle of Gettysburg on July 14, 1863, at what spot in Maryland?
    A. Rushing Waters
    B. Falling Waters
    C. Sandy Run

40. Born in 1828 at his family's Pitt County plantation Grimesland, Major General Bryan Grimes lived until 1880 when an assassin killed him at home. During the Civil War, Grimes distinguished himself on many fields including what battle marked by Stonewall Jackson's famous "flank march?"
    A. Bull Run
    B. Seven Pines
    C. Chancellorsville

41. Lieutenant General Daniel Harvey Hill was an outspoken Tar Heel whose criticism of superior Braxton Bragg cost him a promotion. A man of many talents, Hill wrote a math textbook, engaged in literary pursuits, and was prewar superintendent at the North Carolina Military Institute in what town?
A. Charlotte
B. Greensboro
C. Raleigh

42. A Princeton graduate, Brigadier General Lawrence O'Bryan Branch was born in 1820 and had a prewar career as president of the Raleigh and Gaston Railroad. Branch was killed at the Battle of Antietam on September 17, 1862. Fort Branch in what North Carolina county bears his name?
A. Bertie County
B. Martin County
C. Hyde County

43. Brigadier General Rufus Barringer practiced law in Charlotte after the Civil War, was a member of First Presbyterian Church there, and helped organize the public library in town. A veteran of 76 actions during the war, Barringer was born in what county northeast of Mecklenburg?
A. Lincoln
B. Union
C. Cabarrus

44. Born in 1818 in Guilford County, Major General Jeremy Gilmer was chief engineer in the Confederate Army. Although he survived the war and went on to become a railroad leader, Gilmer nearly died after being wounded on April 6, 1862, during what big battle in Mississippi that also goes by the name of Pittsburg Landing?
A. Shiloh
B. Pear Ridge
C. Chickamauga

45. Born in Sampson County in 1804, Lieutenant General Theophilus Holmes served in the Western Theater of operations during the Civil War. On July 4, 1863, he led an unsuccessful attack on the town of Helena, Arkansas, in an attempt to relieve Federal pressure on what besieged Mississippi River city?
A. Port Gibson
B. Vicksburg
C. Jackson

46. Confederate Major General William Pender was from Edgecombe County and had served in the U.S. Army before the Civil War broke out. On the second day of the Battle of Gettysburg, Pender was hit by a shell fragment and mortally wounded. What hill at Gettysburg was Pender attacking when he was hit?
A. Snodgrass Hill
B. Henry Hill
C. Cemetery Hill

Of note

47. During the Civil War, what railroad company — previously known as the Wilmington and Raleigh Railroad — took supplies from blockade-running ships to Confederate forces in Virginia and so became known as the "lifeline of the South?"
A. Virginia and Carolina
B. Southern Railway Company
C. Wilmington and Weldon

48. The Civil War added greatly to the toll of ships lost off North Carolina's coast. One vessel purposely sunk on December 24, 1864, by Union forces was the *Louisiana*, which was loaded with powder like a floating bomb and set adrift toward what Confederate fort near Southport?
A. Fort Fisher
B. Fort Macon
C. Fort Branch

49. Probably the most famous shipwreck off the Tar Heel coast is the Union ironclad U.S.S. *Monitor*, which sank as it was being towed toward South Carolina from Fort Monroe, Virginia, on December 30, 1862. Identify the vessel towing the *Monitor*, which was named after the last of the original 13 colonies to join the Union.
A. U.S.S. *Connecticut*
B. U.S.S. *Rhode Island*
C. U.S.S. *New Hampshire*

Answers on page 76.

CHAPTER 5

ROADS, ROUTES, & RAILS

*By air, by land, and by sea, we proudly recognize
the pioneers and innovations of transportation.*

Blue Ridge Parkway

1. One of the most unusual sections of mountain terrain in North Carolina can be seen near Milepost 418.8 at the Graveyard Fields Overlook. This somewhat barren landscape has hiking trails and is bisected by the Yellowstone Prong of East Fork Pigeon River. Graveyard Fields Overlook is also near what shimmering mountain?
   A. Mirror Mountain
   B. Looking Glass Rock
   C. Silver Mountain

2. At Milepost 431.4, folks can cast eyes across miles of mountainous splendor at Richland Balsam Overlook. Located near the town of Waynesville, this overlook is at what elevation, the highest point on the Blue Ridge Parkway?
   A. 4,500 feet
   B. 6,053 feet
   C. 6,684 feet

3. Four states can be seen on a clear day from the Waterrock Knob Overlook and visitor station at Milepost 451.2. Waterrock Knob is located on the border of which two North Carolina counties?

A. Haywood/Jackson
B. Swain/Graham
C. Haywood/Madison

4. At Milepost 461.9 in Swain County, Big Witch Overlook at an elevation of 4,160 feet affords an excellent view of the surrounding hardwood forests. Big Witch Overlook is about eight miles from what important tourist center?
   A. Bryson City
   B. Dillsboro
   C. Cherokee

5. Devil's Courthouse Overlook at Milepost 422.4 sits at an altitude of 5,462 feet. A half-mile hike from the parking lot takes visitors to the "Courthouse" for a stunning view. Devil's Courthouse is located in what county?
   A. Buncombe County
   B. Transylvania County
   C. Clay County

6. Taking its name from the nearby 6,032-foot-tall peak, Yellow Face Overlook is in Jackson County at Milepost 450.2. Yellow Face Mountain is part of what range, the first name of which is similar to our official North Carolina state dog.
   A. Plott Balsams

B. Blue Tick Ridge
C. Beagle Balsams

7. A unique spot on the Blue Ridge Parkway at Milepost 433.3 is the Roy Taylor Overlook at 5,580 feet. This overlook is especially geared for the handicapped and is located in what gap named for a type of tree that makes excellent fence posts?
A. Cottonwood Gap
B. Sourwood Gap
C. Locust Gap

8. At Milepost 468.4, Oconaluftee River Overlook affords a view of the famed river that runs through Cherokee and its surroundings. This overlook is just a half-mile from the Blue Ridge Parkway's North Carolina terminus at its junction with what highway?
A. U.S. Highway 441
B. U.S. Highway 19/23
C. N.C. Highway 28

9. Milepost 310, not far from Linville, is the location of Lost Cove Overlook. This parking spot is said to provide an excellent view of a ridge that features what mysterious phenomenon made famous in a song by Tommy Faile?
A. Devil's Tramping Grounds

B. Maco Light
C. Brown Mountain Lights

10. Literary buffs will enjoy the view from Cold Mountain Overlook at Milepost 411.85. Cold Mountain is not only a 6,030-foot-tall peak in Haywood County but also the name of a best-selling novel by what author?
A. Ernest Hemingway
B. F. Scott Fitzgerald
C. Charles Frazier

Engines and tracks

11. Once running between Johnson City, Tennessee, and Boone, the narrow-gauge East Tennessee and Western North Carolina line acquired what nickname that lives on today at a mountain amusement park?
A. Tweetsie
B. Tootles
C. Whistler

12. What is the name of the tycoon who founded not only American Tobacco Company but also the Piedmont and Northern Railway?
A. R.J. Reynolds
B. James Buchanan Duke
C. William Rand Kenan

13. As of 1990, about how many miles of track were owned and maintained by the railroad companies serving North Carolina?
   A. 6,000 miles
   B. 5,000 miles
   C. 4,000 miles

14. Alexander Railroad Company is headquartered in what town that is also the seat of Alexander County?
   A. Hiddenite
   B. Taylorsville
   C. Millersville

15. What state agency has jurisdiction over railroad operations in North Carolina?
   A. North Carolina Department of Transportation
   B. North Carolina Utilities Commission
   C. North Carolina Department of Travel and Tourism

16. In what year did Piedmont and Northern Railway begin the switch from electric to diesel-powered engines?
   A. 1950
   B. 1955
   C. 1960

17. Known as the "Mullet Line," what railroad company served the burgeoning coastal fishing industry during the 1800s?
   A. Virginia and Carolina
   B. Atlantic and North Carolina Railroad
   C. Wilmington and Raleigh Railroad

18. In what year did the North Carolina Railroad Company complete the full 223-mile route that ran between Raleigh, Goldsboro, and Charlotte?
   A. 1856
   B. 1899
   C. 1870

19. What Alamance County town began as a repair-shop site for North Carolina Railroad Company?
   A. Burlington
   B. Alamance
   C. Haw River

20. Formed in 1894, this railroad company quickly obtained extensive track rights and soon dominated rail business in the Piedmont.
   A. Virginia and Carolina Railroad
   B. Southern Railway Company
   C. Northeastern Railroad

21. What North Carolina city became the first in the state to operate an electric street railway?
A. Wilmington
B. Charlotte
C. Asheville

22. North Carolina's worst rail disaster took place on December 16, 1943, when two Atlantic Coast Line trains collided. The number of dead came to 72 in this horrific crash near what town that is the seat of Robeson County?
A. St. Pauls
B. Maxton
C. Lumberton

Shipwrecks

23. One of the earliest known shipwrecks on the North Carolina coast took place in June 1585 when the flagship of Sir Richard Granville's fleet, the *Tiger*, ran aground in Ocracoke Inlet. Granville's ship was on its way to Sir Walter Raleigh's colonists on what island?
A. Harkers Island
B. Hatteras Island
C. Roanoke Island

24. An unusual North Carolina shipwreck story dates to 1822 and revolves around a horse on board the schooner *Enterprise* that sank near Chicamacomico Banks. Pushed into the water as the boat went down, the steed led passengers ashore about 30 miles north of Hatteras near what modern village?
A. Rodanthe
B. Frisco
C. Buxton

25. In October 1842, a bottle washed up at Shelby Bay, Bermuda, with a note from Captain William Morgan telling of his ship breaking up off Hatteras. Nothing was left of this schooner that disappeared in what Morgan called a "strong North Wester." The ship had what name, which is shared by towns in Massachusetts, North Carolina, and South Carolina?
A. *Concord*
B. *Lexington*
C. *Lowell*

26. In early April 1913, a terrible storm struck the North Carolina coast, bringing snow, high winds, and rough seas. That gale wrecked many ships with names such as *Rob Roy, Clintonia, Edward Luckenbach,* and what other name shared by the wife of the emperor Napoleon?
   A. *Madeline*
   B. *Josephine*
   C. *Marcelle*

27. In 1877, a dramatic shipwreck took place on November 24 when the U.S. man-of-war steamer *Huron* went ashore as it headed for Key West. The *Huron* lost 103 souls after it sank close to what beach near present-day Jockey's Ridge State Park?
   A. Corolla
   B. Duck
   C. Nags Head

28. Loaded with fertilizer, the four-masted schooner *Florence C. Magee* ran aground about 600 yards off Bodie Island on February 26, 1894. Thanks to efforts of lifesavers such as J.T. Etheridge, the crew of 10 men was saved. Mariners today can recognize the Bodie Island lighthouse by what color pattern?

A. Red/white stripes
B. Black/white spiral stripes
C. Black/white horizontal bands

29. On April 6, 1869, a passenger steamship caught fire and sank as it rounded Cape Hatteras on its way to New York. Although the passengers and most of the crew were saved, the cook, two cabin boys, a seaman, and the coal heaver of what vessel, named for a large river in England, perished?
   A. *Thames*
   B. *Moselle*
   C. *Clyde*

30. The schooner *Carroll A. Deering* ran ashore off Cape Hatteras in January 1921. No one was found aboard, thus prompting the tag of "ghost ship." Name the shoals that snagged the mystery vessel that was drifting without a crew.
   A. Diamond Shoals
   B. Mussel Shoals
   C. Gulf Stream Shoals

31. One of North Carolina's saddest disasters took place on December 30, 1883, when a barge carrying prison laborers capsized in the Tuckasegee River, and 20 men drowned. They had been part of a crew

working on a railroad tunnel near what Jackson County town that is currently a stop on the Great Smoky Mountain Railway?

A. Bryson City

B. Waynesville

C. Dillsboro

32. Maritime mayhem took place off Cape Hatteras on the evening of December 31, 1862, when the ironclad ship U.S.S. *Monitor* sank in a storm. Sixteen of the crew drowned, and 49 more were rescued before it went down. What Confederate ironclad, formerly the U.S.S. *Merrimack,* had the U.S.S. *Monitor* fought earlier that year at Hampton Roads, Virginia?

A. C.S.S. *Virginia*

B. C.S.S. *Alabama*

C. C.S.S. *Albemarle*

33. During World War II, Liberty ships were used for hauling everything from cargo to troops. The North Carolina Ship Corporation at Wilmington contributed greatly to the war effort by building 126 Liberties and 232 other ships. The first Liberty ship from the Wilmington yards was launched on December 6, 1941, and had what name?

A. U.S.S. *Zebulon B. Vance*

B. U.S.S. *Elwood P. Suggins*

C. U.S.S. *Josephus Daniels*

Up in the air

34. According to legend, the first North Carolinian to "fly" was a Native American "great conjurer" named Roncommock who put a river reed in his mouth and "flew" over Salmon Creek in the early 1700s. Roncommock was a member of which Indian tribe that gave its name to a river and county whose seat is Edenton?

A. Currituck

B. Chowan

C. Perquimans

35. Ballooning was part of the pre-Wright brothers Tar Heel aviation scene. In 1889, a man named C.K. Perry became North Carolina's first aviation fatality when his balloon collapsed at a show and he was fatally injured. Perry crashed in what town situated on the Catawba River in Gaston County?

A. Lowell

B. Cherryville

C. Mount Holly

36. North Carolina's first female aeronaut was a petite Charlotte native named Delia Jaquin who joined Frank Zeno's air show in 1892. For the next several years, Jaquin, under what name, made many daring parachute jumps from balloons?
A. Little Dot Zeno
B. Jumping Jaquin Flash
C. Delia the Daredevil

37. In the 1870s, Hertford County was a site of aviation experimentation when the brother of machine-gun inventor Richard Gatling built an airplane of oak splints and wire that was nicknamed "turkey buzzard." What was the name of Gatling's brother who built this experimental craft?
A. John Paul Gatling
B. Whit Sanders Gatling
C. James Henry Gatling

38. Born in Taylorsville in 1816, Dr. Daniel Asbury is said to have constructed an aircraft powered by steam. The craft supposedly looked like a torpedo with wings and had a basket beneath. Asbury's plan to fly the contraption was announced in what still-published Charlotte newspaper in early 1881?

A. *The Charlotte Observer*
B. *The Charlotte News*
C. *The Charlotte Citizen-Times*

39. William Wallace Christmas (1865-1960), a man of many talents, was an award-winning artist, musician, and inventor. Christmas is said to have constructed numerous large aircraft models, a kite that was 11 feet long, and a glider. Christmas hailed from which Warren County town, also the county seat?
A. Fishing Creek
B. Warrenton
C. Roanoke

40. Born in Carteret County in 1869 and at an early age known for his mechanical abilities, Luther Paul was an early advocate of helicopters. Paul constructed one around the time of the Wrights' 1903 flight, and it reportedly lifted several feet off the ground in 1907. Paul gave his machine what name after its ability to hover?
A. Marsh Hen
B. Hummingbird
C. Bumble Bee

41. W.F. Johnson was the first African American to design an

airplane on the basis of his wooden model that won a first prize in 1910. Constructed with two propellers and an electric motor, Johnson's plane took the prize at what Guilford County event?

A. North Carolina State Fair
B. Greensboro Central Carolina Fair
C. Rocky Mount Exhibition of 1910

42. Lindsey Hopkins from Rockingham County was an early aviation entrepreneur. In 1911, Hopkins bought two Curtiss planes. His pilot, Thornwell Andrews, has been called our state's first professional aviator. Hopkins later held a position at what company that built the P-51 Mustang WWII fighter?

A. Boeing
B. North American Aviation
C. Douglas Aircraft

43. A graduate of the North Carolina College of Agriculture and Mechanic Arts and a native of Lenoir, James Spainhour designed a monoplane in 1911. After he gave up flying, Spainhour worked on the Manhattan Project that produced what weapon?

A. Guided missile
B. Laser beam
C. Atomic bomb

Hit the road

44. This three-digit roadway has a junction with N.C. Highway 411 in Sampson County and passes through towns such as Magnolia, Kenansville, Kornegay, LaGrange, and Maury before it ends up crossing the Virginia state line at Lake Gaston. Name this road that also passes near the Cowan Museum and Liberty Hall in Duplin County.

A. N.C. Highway 111
B. N.C. Highway 903
C. N.C. Highway 222

45. This road runs from Southport on the coast across U.S. Highway 17 and U.S. Highway 74 at Bolton, then continues northwest through Robeson and Hoke counties to Samarcand and Candor. What highway is this that also goes through Lumberton and Raeford?

A. N.C. Highway 131
B. N.C. Highway 211
C. N.C. Highway 710

46. Having the distinction of being the most westward road in our state, this highway is only about 15 miles long and passes through the community of Suit and near Oak Park. Guess the number of this road that crosses into Tennessee near Farner and has its North Carolina terminus near Ranger in Cherokee County.
A. N.C. Highway 294
B. N.C. Highway 141
C. N.C. Highway 116

47. A popular back road for folks traveling to the lower coast of our state from the Piedmont, this highway has one end at Ocean Isle Beach and the other at N.C. Highway 130 in Robeson County. What is the number of this byway that passes through communities such as Longwood, Cherry Grove, and Fair Bluff?
A. N.C. Highway 130
B. N.C. Highway 905
C. N.C. Highway 904

48. Sylva in Jackson County marks one end of this highway that traverses the Nantahala National Forest and then enters South Carolina and Sumter National Forest. Identify this roadway that goes though towns such as Tuckasegee, Glenville, and High Hampton and skirts the shore of Thorpe Lake.
A. N.C. Highway 215
B. N.C. Highway 107
C. N.C. Highway 106

49. Hot Springs in Madison County is the start of this road that runs in a southerly direction toward Lake Junaluska, U.S. Highway 74, Interstate 40, and Waynesville. Along the way, it passes through Spring Creek, Trust, and Luck. Give a number to the highway that also visits Crabtree.
A. N.C. Highway 209
B. N.C. Highway 212
C. N.C. Highway 197

50. Located in the northeast section of our state, this three-numbered highway starts out in Louisburg in Franklin County, continues through into Hertford County, and ends at a junction with N.C. Highway 45 at Harrellsville. What road is this that also passes through St. John and Ahoskie?
A. N.C. Highway 561
B. N.C. Highway 305
C. N.C. Highway 142

51. Chatham County contains all 20 miles of this highway that starts just south of Bennett at a junction with N.C. Highway 22, goes through the community of Bear Creek, and crosses the Rocky River. Give the three-digit designation of the road that has its other end at Pittsboro.
A. N.C. Highway 705
B. N.C. Highway 157
C. N.C. Highway 902

52. Passing through Iredell, Rowan, and Davie counties, this roadway forms a large half circle on its route through towns such as Mount Ulla, Bear Poplar, Advance, and Farmington. Give the correct three digits for the highway that has one end at Mooresville and the other at a junction with U.S. Highway 601.
A. N.C. Highway 136
B. N.C. Highway 801
C. N.C. Highway 127

53. Routed through Watauga and Ashe counties, this three-digit North Carolina state highway crosses the North Fork of the New River and visits towns such as Helton, Baldwin, and Todd. What road is this that runs through Boone to the Virginia state line?
A. N.C. Highway 194
B. N.C. Highway 113
C. N.C. Highway 163

Answers on page 77.

CHAPTER 6

NATURAL HERITAGE

*Lakes and rivers, forests and fields — nature has provided
us with a wealth of beauty to treasure.*

Out on a limb

1. The large, heart-shaped leaves of this tree are not only good for shade but also provide food for caterpillars that are used for fishing bait. Name this tree that is a member of the bignonia family, produces a long, bean-like seedpod, and is sometimes referred to as a "cigar tree."
   A. Crape myrtle
   B. Catalpa
   C. Catawba

2. A member of the witch-hazel family, this widespread tree produces star-shaped leaves; round, spiky seedpods; and fragrant buds. Also known as liquidambar, what tree has served such diverse purposes as hiding places for runaway slaves and cabinetmaking?
   A. Tupelo
   B. Basswood
   C. Sweetgum

3. Leaves on this common tree, a member of the laurel family, are about four to six inches long and have two to five rounded lobes. Long used by American Indians as a source of medicine, the leaves, bark, and roots of what fragrant tree can be used in tea and other recipes?
   A. Sassafras
   B. Juniper
   C. Yaupon

4. Called thorn tree by some, this member of the pulse family has alternate, compound leaves seven to eight inches long that are characterized by an even number of leaflets. In addition to thorns, another feature of which tree is its foot-long, flat seedpods that can be dried to make rattles?
   A. Honey locust
   B. Coffee tree
   C. Bean tree

5. Often found in swampy or shady areas, this tree has simple leaves four to 12 inches long that are pointed at the apex and taper to the base. Also called custard apple, what tree has maroon flowers as well as edible fruit that has a pulpy consistency?
   A. Persimmon
   B. Mock orange
   C. Papaw

6. Found in the yards of many older homes in our state and also along roadsides where its feathery leaves and fluffy pink flowers give an exotic appearance, which native of Asia, sometimes called the silk tree, is also a member of

the legume family?

A. Chinaberry

B. Sugarberry

C. Mimosa

7. Measuring up to three feet long and more than one foot wide, the leaves of this relatively rare tree were spotted in Gaston County around 1795 by noted French botanist André Michaux. Name the tree that produces these huge leaves and equally impressive white flowers.

A. Giant laurel

B. Bigleaf magnolia

C. French rhododendron

8. Known in some parts as the Carolina poplar, this tree has delta-shaped leaves with jagged edges. Most often found along streambeds, lowlands, and swamps, what tree can grow several feet each year and produces spring flowers that hang in long fronds?

A. Cottonwood

B. White willow

C. Cypress

9. The ebony family includes a member found in most parts of our state. What tree with oval-shaped leaves about four to six inches long provides wood for billiard cues and golf-club heads and yellowsh fruit for everything from beer to cakes?

A. Serviceberry

B. Persimmon

C. Chinquapin

10. Often found scattered across woodlands and fields, this small tree has unlobed, heart-shaped leaves about five inches long. Also called the Judas tree and a member of the pulse family, name the tree whose flowers are especially conspicuous in the spring when they are among the first to appear.

A. Dogwood

B. Basswood

C. Redbud

Talk to the animals

11. One of the most popular attractions at Grandfather Mountain was a black bear that arrived in 1968 and entertained and educated visitors until her death in 1993. Name this 400-pound animal whose image appeared on television, billboards, and in magazines.

A. Hilda

B. Wilma

C. Mildred

12. During his long career as a cowboy personality and kid-show host on WBTV, Fred Kirby of Charlotte was often seen on his faithful horse. Kirby's steed, which was a regular feature of the "Carolinas' Carrousel Parade," had what name reminiscent of a type of colorful cloth?
A. Calico
B. Madras
C. Paisley

13. The first elephant of her type to be born in the Western Hemisphere, "Little Diamond" came to the N.C. Zoological Park in 1995 from the Knoxville Zoo. What type of elephant is this popular pachyderm characterized by very large ears?
A. Indian elephant
B. African elephant
C. Pygmy elephant

14. In April 1997, a chimpanzee named Sidney escaped from the Charlotte Metro Zoo and led folks on a merry chase for a week before being captured. What Rowan County community was the site of Sidney's big adventure?
A. China Grove
B. New London
C. Rockwell

15. An episode of "The Andy Griffith Show" featured a goat named Jimmy that stirred up Mayberry when it consumed a volatile substance. To get Jimmy out of town, Barney played his harmonica like the Pied Piper. What did folks think Jimmy had ingested?
A. Moonshine
B. Black powder
C. Dynamite

16. A longtime and famous resident of the N.C. Museum of Natural Sciences was a 16-foot Burmese python that Master Sergeant Dewey Simpson brought home from Vietnam in 1963. This popular snake, viewed by thousands of museum visitors before his death in 1989, had what name similar to that of a member of the Beatles?
A. Ringo
B. George
C. John

17. The Charlotte Nature Museum has had some unusual animals in its care over the years, including a two-headed yellow-bellied slider turtle believed to be the only one of its kind on display in the nation. This example of bicephalism was named after what popular sandwich combo?
A. Peanut Butter and Jelly

B. Swiss Cheese and Ham

C. Pimento and Cheese

18. The University of North Carolina has had a ram as its mascot since 1924 when the university's business manager Charlie Woollen put up $25 to acquire the first one. A UNC tradition ever since, the many rams who played their part on the sidelines have all had what name?

A. Rambo

B. Rameses

C. Ramie

19. Great apes and the N.C. Zoological Park have proved a winning combination for many years. A former TV commercial star, Ramar was the zoo's first gorilla resident. In March 1989, the N.C. Zoo had another premier when its first baby gorilla was born. This bundle of joy was named after what African-American cultural celebration?

A. Kwanzaa

B. Mgumba

C. Echukwu

Watering holes

20. The first hydroelectric dam in North Carolina was built in 1898 by the Fries Manufacturing and Power Company. Known as the Idols Dam, this structure was constructed across what river that begins in Watauga County and eventually meets the Pee Dee River?

A. Yadkin River

B. New River

C. French Broad River

21. The largest man-made body of water in the state, Lake Norman began filling in 1963 with the construction of a dam across the Catawba River. Name the dam that is 7,387 feet long and built near the site of a Revolutionary War battle at the Mecklenburg/Lincoln county line.

A. Duke's Ford

B. Cowans Ford

C. Tharpe's Ford

22. At 480 feet tall, Fontana Dam in Graham County is the tallest in the eastern United States. The dam forms 10,530-acre Fontana Lake and was built by the Tennessee Valley Authority during what years?

A. 1929 to 1933

B. 1934 to 1939

C. 1941 to 1945

23. This dam was built in 1917 to furnish electrical power for an Alcoa Aluminum plant at Narrows of the Yadkin in Stanly County. Name the dam that stands more than 200 feet high and has impounded a popular lake of nearly 6,000 acres near the Uwharrie National Forest.
A. Badin Lake Dam
B. High Rock Lake Dam
C. Lake Norman Dam

24. Duke Power's Lookout Shoals Dam went into operation in 1915 on the Catawba River near Claremont. In what year did the most destructive flood ever on the Catawba River not only wash away all but one bridge, but also completely submerge the dam for a time?
A. 1916
B. 1918
C. 1920

25. Originally constructed in 1911 by Rockingham Power Company, Blewett Falls Dam was taken over by Carolina Power and Light in 1926. This 1,650-foot-long dam forms a 2,500-acre lake on the Pee Dee River near what Anson County town?
A. Polkton
B. Lilesville
C. Marshville

26. Tillery Hydro Plant on the Yadkin River began generating power in 1928 and formed Lake Tillery. This 2,800-foot-long dam now named for the first president of CP&L, was first named after what Stanly County town on its western shore?
A. Lambert
B. Rockwell
C. Norwood

27. When this Duke Power dam on the Catawba River began operation in 1923, it was one of the first built to produce electricity for homes rather than strictly for industrial use. Name this structure located near Mount Holly that forms a 3,000-acre lake bordering Gaston and Mecklenburg counties.
A. Mountain Island Dam
B. Mountain Lake Dam
C. Mountain Creek Dam

See shells

28. This shell can be as long as four inches and has reddish-brown spots, as well as ridges along its length. Home to a type of snail and a prize to collectors, what shell was declared the official North Carolina state seashell by

the General Assembly in 1965?
A. Scotch bonnet
B. Leopard shell
C. Helmet shell

29. Often found on our North Carolina coast, the scallop is a mollusk similar to a clam. Scallop shells have an oval shape with two ear-like flanges at the hinge. There are three types of scallops along our coast, and all are fished commercially. These include the bay scallop, sea scallop, and what type whose multi-colored shell resembles a type of cloth?
A. Silk scallop
B. Denim scallop
C. Calico scallop

30. Cylindrical in shape and up to three inches long, the olive shell is grayish-tan with darker zigzag markings. The gastropod that lives in the olive shell feeds on other shell-dwellers such as clams and mussels. The olive shell is the official seashell of what state?
A. Florida
B. South Carolina
C. Georgia

31. A familiar sight along the North Carolina shoreline, this shell is wedge-shaped, less than an inch long, and comes in an endless variety of colors. A bivalve, the animal that lives in these prolific little shells feeds on plankton strained from the water. Name this shell that can be boiled into a tasty broth.
A. Rainbow shell
B. Midget shell
C. Coquina clam

32. Among the largest shells found along the North Carolina coast, this type is shaped like a twisted pear and can grow to 12 inches long. The home of a large marine snail that can be used in chowder, what shell will also make a fairly good signal horn?
A. Whelk
B. Trumpet shell
C. Ram's horn shell

33. Up to 10 inches long and fan-shaped, pen shells are so thin that they can sometimes be translucent. Besides providing a nice addition to a shell collection, pen shells offer edible meat from the animal inside, fibers that in Europe are sometimes made into cloth, and occasionally what other feature?
A. Teeth
B. Pearls
C. Fins

34. With a length about six times its width, this type of shell is often found buried just below the sand where the mollusk burrows with an external foot. A look at the shell gives a hint of what some folks say Native Americans used it for. Sometimes called the Atlantic jackknife clam, this shell also goes by what name?
    A. Carolina cutter
    B. Indian scraper shell
    C. Atlantic razor clam

35. With a shiny surface, rounded shape, and coloration that ranges from brownish to silver, jingle shells resemble bright coins on the beach. The animal inside a jingle shell is a bivalve that attaches itself to most any underwater object. It is said that sailors in the old days gave jingle shells what other name?
    A. Mermaid's toenails
    B. Doubloon shell
    C. Nickel shell

36. Often called the hard-shelled clam, this important shell and its animal inhabitant have provided man with food, a medium of exchange in the form of wampum, and simple tools. Boasting a potential life span of 40 years if it can escape predators and hungry seafood lovers, the hard-shelled clam also goes by what name?
    A. Chowder clam
    B. Quahog
    C. Atlantic clam

Creepy crawlies

37. The American chameleon lizard is a common resident of North Carolina with the uncommon traits of being able to change color and regenerate its tail should the need arise. Usually a bright green hue, this reptile also goes by what name?
    A. Gecko
    B. Salamander
    C. Anole

38. When frightened, the North Carolina snake *Heterodon platirhinos* usually puffs itself up in a bluffing manner or rolls over and plays dead. Growing up to three feet in length and having a mottled scale pattern of orange, black, brown, and yellow, this reptile's unusual nose gives it what common name?
    A. Snub-nose snake
    B. Hog-nose snake
    C. Blunt-nose snake

39. Since 1979, the turtle, whose scientific name is *Terrapene*

carolina, has been North Carolina's official state reptile. Living up to 40 years, with the ability to move the forward portion of its plastron to the carapace, this inhabitant of field and forest goes by what common name?
A. Gopher tortoise
B. Eastern box turtle
C. Snapping turtle

40. Often observed scurrying around Tar Heel back porches or across logs in search of insects, *Plestiodon fasciatus* has a dark brown back accented with pale stripes and a bright blue tail. Name this common North Carolina lizard that can grow to four inches in length.
A. Blue-tailed skink
B. Blue-tailed skank
C. Five-lined salamander

41. Generally found in North Carolina mountain streams and rivers, the giant salamander amphibian *Cryptobranchus alleganiensis* can grow as large as two feet in length. This gnarly creature has brown, wrinkled skin with yellowish or black spots and goes by what common name?
A. River devil
B. Hellbender
C. Devil lizard

42. Another type of North Carolina salamander is found only in or near the Neuse River, hence the name Neuse River water dog. With the coloration of a gray back and russet stomach and with four toes on each foot, *Necturus lewisi* grows to what length?
A. 15-20 inches
B. 12-15 inches
C. 6-9 inches

43. A commonly seen and heard frog in North Carolina, *Rana utricularia* is a resident of the coastal and Piedmont regions, grows to four inches in length, is usually green, and has large, black spots. These spots give rise to what common name?
A. Polka dot frog
B. Leopard frog
C. Harlequin frog

44. *Rana capito* is a North Carolina frog generally found in the sandhills region. A nocturnal creature with brownish, wrinkled skin, this three-inch-long frog goes by what name due to its habit of living in a hole in the ground?
A. Mole frog
B. Burrow frog
C. Gopher frog

Answers on page 78.

CHAPTER 7

SPIRIT
OF THE
SEASON

*There's a whole lot going on in December —
holidays and history, trees and special events.*

O, Christmas tree

1. The most popular type of Christmas tree in North America, and the type that accounts for more than 95 percent of those grown in our state, was discovered by 19th-century British botanist John Fraser. Known as *Abies fraseri*, this tree is native to the southeastern United States and has what common name?
   A. Fraser pine
   B. Fraser spruce
   C. Fraser fir

2. Christmas trees from North Carolina are not only displayed in the United States but also are shipped to places as far away as Japan. A labor-intensive plant to produce, a typical Christmas tree takes about how many years to grow from seedling to market-ready size?
   A. 4 years
   B. 7-12 years
   C. 20 years

3. Five western North Carolina counties grow 88 percent of the state's total production of Christmas trees. Besides Avery, Watauga, Jackson, and Allegheny, what county, whose seat is Jefferson, leads the way in Christmas tree production?
   A. Ashe County
   B. Cherokee County
   C. Wilkes County

4. Two-thirds of North Carolina's Christmas tree farms are operations that are 10 or fewer acres in size. On the other hand, the 60 largest farms have 100 or more acres. Growing about 1,400 trees on each acre, what is the average size of a North Carolina Christmas tree farm?
   A. 70 acres
   B. 50 acres
   C. 15 acres

5. On a national level, North Carolina ranks first in the number of dollars made for each Christmas tree sold. In terms of annual receipts for Christmas tree sales, our state's total of $99 million ranks second only to what West Coast state?
   A. California
   B. Oregon
   C. Washington

6. Besides *Abies fraseri*, there are several other types of Christmas trees grown in North Carolina. One species is known by the scientific name *Pinus strobus*

and the common name of Eastern white pine. Another variety is *Picea abies*, which goes by what common name that is similar to a European country whose capital is Oslo?

A. Norway spruce
B. Swedish pine
C. Swiss fir

7. One of the most meaningful and unique ways to get a North Carolina Christmas tree for your home is to actually go out to the farm, hike the fields, and cut one yourself. In 2004, North Carolina had about how many "cut your own" farms where families can enjoy this activity?

A. 150 locations
B. 250 locations
C. 400 locations

8. Supporting the claim that North Carolina Fraser fir Christmas trees are the best, the National Christmas Tree Association has picked one to be placed in the White House nine times — more than any other state. The first time a North Carolina Fraser fir decorated the White House was in 1971, when which president was in office?

A. Richard Nixon
B. Jimmy Carter
C. Gerald Ford

9. Besides providing pleasure during the holiday season, North Carolina Christmas trees are also ecologically friendly in recycled uses such as fishing "reefs" and mulch. Another ecological plus is that an acre of growing Christmas trees puts enough oxygen back in the atmosphere to supply the needs of how many people?

A. 10 people
B. 18 people
C. 100 people

Special events

10. The annual Moravian Christmas celebration at Old Salem has roots that date back to mid-18th century Germany. For more than 250 years, Moravian children have been given what object on Christmas Eve to make the spirit bright?

A. Lighted candle
B. Candy cane
C. Carved reindeer

11. One of the largest holiday season light shows in the nation takes place each year at Tanglewood Park near Clemmons. Besides dozens of animated displays and toy soldiers, Tanglewood has three miles of decorations featuring approximately how many lights?
   A. 100,000
   B. 200,000
   C. 1,000,000

12. December will see Christmas by Candlelight with tours, music, and refreshments at the Duke Homestead State Historic Site. In addition to the restored mid-19th-century Washington Duke home, what other interesting facility is on this site?
   A. Railway depot
   B. Tobacco museum
   C. College chapel

13. Each year, Hilton Park in Wilmington holds the annual lighting of what it claims is the "world's largest living Christmas tree." Name the type of tree that's the center of attention at this event that also includes music, entertainment, and Santa.
   A. White cedar
   B. Fraser fir
   C. Live oak

14. An annual tradition, candlelight tours and colonial revival decorations will be part of Christmas at Tryon Palace Historic Sites and Gardens this December. The restored residence of North Carolina colonial Governor William Tryon and our state's first capitol, Tryon Palace is located in what town?
   A. New Bern
   B. Morehead City
   C. Beaufort

15. Folks interested in seeing how a Civil War soldier spent his Christmas holiday can take part in the December candlelight tour of one of the best preserved 19th-century forts in the United States. Located in Martin County, name this bastion near the town of Hamilton.
   A. Fort Caswell
   B. Fort Branch
   C. Fort Fisher

16. Christmas at Biltmore Estate near Asheville means a season of lavish decorations and holiday beauty enjoyed by thousands of visitors. The original owner of Biltmore Estate, George Vanderbilt, held the official opening of his

mansion on Christmas Eve in what year?

A. 1895
B. 1910
C. 1901

17. The town of Canton in Haywood County kicks off its annual Christmas holiday Festival of Lights with a nighttime parade. Canton also goes by what promotional nickname that reflects an important industry there?

A. Saw Mill Village
B. Mica Town
C. Papertown, USA

18. Dillsboro in Jackson County is one North Carolina mountain town that goes all out at Christmas with lights, luminaries, and fancifully decorated gift shops. The railroad that stops in Dillsboro even gets into the act with a Santa Express. Name this railway that also chugs into Bryson City.

A. Blue Ridge Railroad
B. Great Smoky Mountains Railroad
C. Western N.C. Railroad

19. Started in 1954 by the Charlotte Choral Society, the annual performance of the Singing Christmas Tree is sung by Carolina voices in what Queen City cultural center?

A. Charlotte Coliseum
B. Park Center
C. Ovens Auditorium

20. Folks who want to cut their own Christmas tree and have some fun while they're at it should remember the Annual Choose and Cut Christmas Tree Day in Alleghany County. What town, the seat of Allegheny County, sponsors this event?

A. Jefferson
B. Mouth of Wilson
C. Sparta

21. Besides its annual Country Christmas musical celebration, the town of Kenansville also holds a holiday candle tour of what county?

A. Onslow County
B. Hyde County
C. Duplin County

22. Smithfield in Johnston County enjoys its big annual Christmas parade each December. Also celebrated in Smithfield is the Christmas Eve birth of film star Ava Gardner who was born in nearby Grabtown in what year?
A. 1922
B. 1935
C. 1940

23. The Beaufort by the Sea Carolina Christmas Walk highlights many of the restored colonial-era homes and inns in Beaufort that are open for visitors to tour and enjoy by foot or from an English double-decker bus. One of North Carolina's most historic towns, Beaufort was laid out in what year?
A. 1700
B. 1715
C. 1745

24. Located in McDowell County, Old Fort is the scene of the annual Christmas Meals at the Depot event and a holiday parade. The depot celebration will include homemade mountain food. Old Fort is located near the beginning of what river?

A. Pigeon River
B. Catawba River
C. Horsepasture River

25. One of the most unique Christmas celebrations in North Carolina is the Lake Lure Boat Parade. Boats decorated with holiday lights cruise the lake, and participants later enjoy a fireworks show. The Lake Lure Boat Parade takes place in the shadow of what mountain?
A. Black Mountain
B. Crowders Mountain
C. Rumbling Bald Mountain

26. In Wilmington, what is called the "world's largest living Christmas tree" will be lit. Organized by the Wilmington Recreation Division, the tree lighting will also include music and a visit from Santa. About how old is the "world's largest living Christmas tree"?
A. 400 years old
B. 200 years old
C. 150 years old

27. The restored 1825 home and grounds of the Malcolm Blue Farm and Museum hosts its Christmas Open House with caroling, period decorations, and refreshments. Listed on the National Register of

Historic Places, Malcolm Blue Farm is located on Bethesda Road in what Moore County town named for a Scottish seaport?

A. Edinburgh
B. Cameron
C. Aberdeen

28. The North Carolina Arboretum celebrates a "Southern Appalachian Christmas" with crafts, music, and other holiday exhibits throughout the month of December. The arboretum was founded in 1986 on 426 acres near Asheville and what national forest?

A. Cherokee National Forest
B. Pisgah National Forest
C. Uwharrie National Forest

29. December brings one of the most unusual holiday events to North Carolina when the "Christmas Howling" comes to the Alligator River National Wildlife refuge near Manteo. "Howlers" meet with park rangers to try their luck calling up what species of wild canine found there?

A. Red wolf
B. Dingo
C. Kit fox

30. Another North Carolina coastal holiday happening is the annual Christmas by the Sea Festival in the Oak Island/Southport area. Held on successive weekends in December, this series of events includes home tours and a lighted boat flotilla. In addition to N.C. Highway 211, Southport can be accessed by ferry from what historic site?

A. Fort Macon
B. Fort Fisher
C. Fort Beauregard

Answers on page 79.

ANSWERS

CHAPTER 1: BIRDS & BUDS

1. B. Solomon's seal
2. C. Yucca
3. A. Soapwort
4. C. Bull bay
5. B. Thunderwood
6. A. Maypop
7. C. Wild carrot
8. A. Apple of Peru
9. A. Chicory
10. C. Black-eyed Susan
11. B. Cow lily
12. A. Blue Ridge Parkway
13. C. 500 species
14. A. Hayes Cabin
15. B. Benjamin Duke
16. C. Fort Raleigh
17. C. Department of Horticultural Science
18. A. Pinehurst
19. B. Cape Fear River
20. A. Wrightsville Sound
21. B. *Horn in the West*
22. A. Osprey
23. C. American oystercatcher
24. B. Starling
25. A. Shrike
26. B. Wild turkey
27. B. Painted bunting
28. C. American goldfinch
29. A. Common nighthawk
30. A. Orton Plantation
31. A. Hugh Morton
32. B. Tony Bennett
33. A. R. Gregg Cherry
34. B. Bellamy Mansion
35. C. Thalian Hall

CHAPTER 2: STATE FARE

1. A. Lexington Barbecue
2. C. Sanitary Fish Market
3. B. Yum Yum Better Ice Cream
4. B. Cheerwine
5. A. Krispy Kreme
6. B. 25 percent
7. A. Cucumber and Vine
8. C. Texas Pete
9. B. 1903
10. A. Slim Jim
11. C. Moravia
12. B. Smithfield
13. B. Goldsboro
14. B. 40 percent
15. A. Duplin County
16. B. 225 eggs
17. A. 46
18. B. 4th place
19. C. Scuppernong
20. A. 17,000 pounds
21. A. Dillsboro
22. C. Ashe
23. A. National Register of Historic Places
24. A. Sears
25. C. Trent River
26. B. Carl Sandburg
27. C. Valle Crucis
28. A. Four Diamond Award
29. B. Grocery
30. C. Bryson City
31. B. Blowing Rock

CHAPTER 3: ABOUT TOWN

1. B. 1739
2. C. Newport River
3. A. 1952
4. C. Southport
5. B. U.S. Highway 70
6. A. Radio Island
7. B. Brevard
8. A. Andrew Jackson
9. C. Albemarle Sound
10. A. Steel
11. B. Avery County
12. C. I-85
13. B. Troy
14. A. Taylorsville
15. C. Grover Cleveland
16. C. Carteret County
17. A. Lord Proprietor of Carolina
18. A. Hornet's nest
19. B. Charlotte Hornets
20. C. Columbia
21. B. D.H. Hill
22. A. Lance Inc.
23. C. Catawba River
24. C. Mecklenburg Declaration of Independence
25. C. WBT
26. A. Camp Greene
27. B. Bandana
28. A. Bearwallow
29. C. Bee Log
30. C. Birdtown
31. A. Horse Shoe
32. B. Loafers Glory
33. C. Lickskillet
34. B. Tuxedo
35. B. Wing
36. C. Sunshine
37. C. Duke University
38. B. Laurel Hill
39. B. Egypt
40. B. Morrisville
41. A. Hillsborough
42. A. Currie

CHAPTER 4: IN UNIFORM

1. C. P-51 Mustang
2. C. Kings Mountain
3. A. Cedar Creek
4. B. Stokes County
5. C. Colonel
6. A. Hindenburg Line
7. B. Iwo Jima
8. A. 5
9. B. Mecklenburg
10. C. Rich Square
11. A. Pee Dee River
12. C. Wilmington
13. A. Joseph Johnston
14. B. Johnston County
15. A. Kilpatrick's Pants
16. B. April 12, 1865
17. A. 26th North Carolina
18. B. Hezekiah Alexander
19. C. House in the Horseshoe
20. A. Belmont Abbey College
21. C. Patrick Ferguson
22. C. Mount Vernon Springs
23. B. Barbecue Church
24. B. Revolutionary War cannon
25. C. Salisbury
26. B. Trojan Regulators

27. A. Pee Dee Wildcats
28. C. Waxhaw Jackson Guards
29. A. Haywood Fire Shooters
30. C. Burke and Catawba Samsons
31. A. Tuckahoe Braves
32. C. Duplin Turpentine Boys
33. B. Nantahala Rangers
34. B. Lone Star Boys
35. A. Scuppernong Grays
36. C. Sandy Run Yellow Jackets
37. A. Haw River Boys
38. B. Caldwell Rough and Ready Boys
39. B. Falling Waters
40. C. Chancellorsville
41. A. Charlotte
42. B. Martin County
43. C. Cabarrus
44. A. Shiloh
45. B. Vicksburg
46. C. Cemetery Hill
47. C. Wilmington and Weldon
48. A. Fort Fisher
49. B. U.S.S. *Rhode Island*

CHAPTER 5:
ROADS, ROUTES, & RAILS

1. B. Looking Glass Rock
2. B. 6,053 feet
3. A. Haywood/Jackson
4. C. Cherokee
5. B. Transylvania County
6. A. Plott Balsams
7. C. Locust Gap
8. A. U.S. Highway 441
9. C. Brown Mountain Lights
10. C. Charles Frazier
11. A. Tweetsie
12. B. James Buchanan Duke
13. C. 4,000 miles
14. B. Taylorsville
15. B. North Carolina Utilities Commission
16. A. 1950
17. B. Atlantic and North Carolina Railroad
18. A. 1856
19. A. Burlington
20. B. Southern Railway Company
21. C. Asheville
22. C. Lumberton
23. C. Roanoke Island
24. A. Rodanthe
25. B. *Lexington*
26. B. *Josephine*
27. C. Nags Head
28. C. Black/white horizontal bands
29. A. *Thames*
30. A. Diamond Shoals
31. C. Dillsboro
32. A. C.S.S. *Virginia*
33. A. U.S.S. *Zebulon B. Vance*
34. B. Chowan
35. C. Mount Holly
36. A. Little Dot Zeno
37. C. James Henry Gatling
38. A. *The Charlotte Observer*
39. B. Warrenton
40. C. Bumble Bee
41. B. Greensboro Central Carolina Fair
42. B. North American Aviation
43. C. Atomic bomb
44. B. N.C. Highway 903
45. B. N.C. Highway 211
46. A. N.C. Highway 294
47. C. N.C. Highway 904
48. B. N.C. Highway 107
49. A. N.C. Highway 209
50. A. N.C. Highway 561
51. C. N.C. Highway 902
52. B. N.C. Highway 801
53. A. N.C. Highway 194

CHAPTER 6: NATURAL HERITAGE

1. B. Catalpa
2. C. Sweetgum
3. A. Sassafras
4. A. Honey locust
5. C. Papaw
6. C. Mimosa
7. B. Bigleaf magnolia
8. A. Cottonwood
9. B. Persimmon
10. C. Redbud
11. C. Mildred
12. A. Calico
13. B. African elephant
14. C. Rockwell
15. C. Dynamite
16. B. George
17. A. Peanut Butter and Jelly
18. B. Rameses
19. A. Kwanzaa
20. A. Yadkin River
21. B. Cowans Ford
22. C. 1941 to 1945

23. A. Badin Lake Dam
24. A. 1916
25. B. Lilesville
26. C. Norwood
27. A. Mountain Island Dam
28. A. Scotch bonnet
29. C. Calico scallop
30. B. South Carolina
31. C. Coquina clam
32. A. Whelk
33. B. Pearls
34. C. Atlantic razor clam
35. A. Mermaid's toenails
36. B. Quahog
37. C. Anole
38. B. Hog-nose snake
39. B. Eastern box turtle
40. A. Blue-tailed skink
41. B. Hellbender
42. C. 6-9 inches
43. B. Leopard frog
44. C. Gopher frog

CHAPTER 7: SPIRIT OF THE SEASON

1. C. Fraser fir
2. B. 7-12 years
3. A. Ashe County
4. C. 15 acres
5. B. Oregon
6. A. Norway spruce
7. C. 400 locations
8. A. Richard Nixon
9. B. 18 people
10. A. Lighted candle
11. C. 1,000,000
12. B. Tobacco museum
13. C. Live oak
14. A. New Bern
15. B. Fort Branch
16. A. 1895

17. C. Papertown, USA
18. B. Great Smoky Mountains Railroad
19. C. Ovens Auditorium
20. C. Sparta
21. C. Duplin County
22. A. 1922
23. B. 1715
24. B. Catawba River
25. C. Rumbling Bald Mountain
26. A. 400 years old
27. C. Aberdeen
28. B. Pisgah National Forest
29. A. Red wolf
30. B. Fort Fisher

Acknowledgements:

Alan Hodge, author of original quizzes for *Our State* magazine; editing by Vicky Jarrett, *Our State* editor in chief, and Elizabeth Hudson, *Our State* senior editor; copy editing by Kim C. Brafford; design and layout by Claudia Royston, *Our State* art director.

Our State's The North Carolina Quiz Book is published by Mann Media Inc., 800 Green Valley Road, Suite 106, Greensboro, N.C. 27408. (800) 948-1409. www.ourstate.com. Single copies, $5.95. Contents copyright 2005 by Mann Media Inc.

Photos:
Front cover
Barbecue sandwich: Transparencies Inc.; Town of Waynesville: Alan Watson; cardinal: Paul Salazar; waterfall: Joseph Boyles.
Back cover
Train: Brian Gomsak; World War II uniform: Mark Wagoner.